Jacqueline

WRITING JOURNAL

ILLUSTRATED BY NICK SHARRATT

DOUBLEDAY

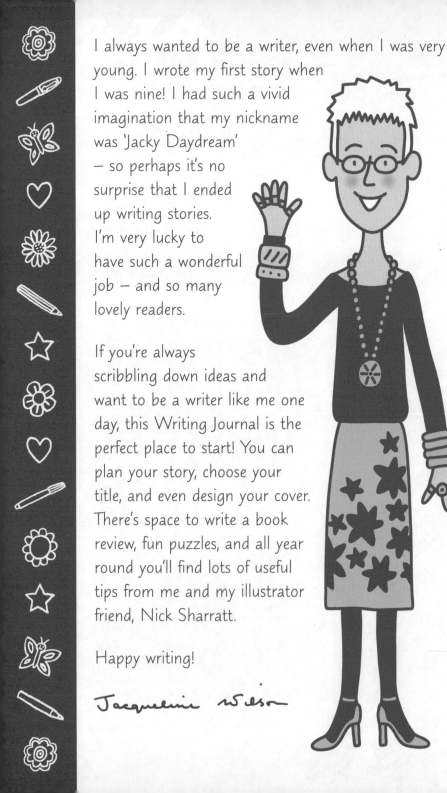

I always wanted to be a writer, even when I was very young. I wrote my first story when I was nine! I had such a vivid imagination that my nickname was 'Jacky Daydream' – so perhaps it's no surprise that I ended up writing stories. I'm very lucky to have such a wonderful job – and so many lovely readers.

If you're always scribbling down ideas and want to be a writer like me one day, this Writing Journal is the perfect place to start! You can plan your story, choose your title, and even design your cover. There's space to write a book review, fun puzzles, and all year round you'll find lots of useful tips from me and my illustrator friend, Nick Sharratt.

Happy writing!

Jacqueline Wilson

THIS WRITING JOURNAL BELONGS TO:

HERE'S A
PHOTO OF
ME!

Name Anna Diane Collins

Address 10 church hill Whaghsburyborough Lincoln LN4 1EJ

Phone Number 07783

Email AnnaDianeCollins@gmail.com

WHAT'S YOUR STORY GOING TO BE ABOUT?

Real-life subjects such as school, friendships and families, like lots of Jacqueline's books? Or maybe you'd rather write a fantasy story, about witches and wizards and fairies? You might already have a brilliant idea whizzing around in your head! If you're not sure where to begin, why not try a story brainstorm? Scribble down your ideas here, and then pick your favourite. Use your imagination!

A boy who is mean to animals wakes up as a dog!

A girl discovers that her goldfish has secret magical powers.

A girl finds out she has a long-lost twin sister, and decides to find her.

Two sisters run away from home after fighting with their mum, and decide to live secretly in their classroom.

NOW IT'S TIME TO SET THE SCENE!

Where is your story going to take place? A tiny cottage in the countryside, with rose bushes in the garden? A posh celebrity mansion? A spooky, haunted castle? Describe or even draw the place — or places — where your story is going to happen. Then, once you begin writing, you'll be able to imagine the scene as clearly as if you were there yourself!

CREATE YOUR MAIN CHARACTER!

This is such an important part of your story. What does she look like? How old is she? Is she brave and feisty like Hetty? Funny and cheeky like Tracy? Quiet and timid like Mandy? You decide! Describe her here — and draw a picture if you like!

_____

_____

_____

_____

_____

_____

_____

_____

WHAT'S YOUR OPENING LINE?

There are lots of different ways to begin a story.
How are you going to begin yours?

You might like to start by introducing your main character –
like in *Hetty Feather*: **My name is Hetty Feather.**
This is a good way to begin, because it means your reader
knows exactly who is going to be telling the story.

You could also use your first line to give readers a little
hint about the story – like in *The Suitcase Kid*:
**When my parents split up they didn't know what to
do with me.** This is a clever way to start, because straight
away your reader learns something very important. In this
case, they know that Andy's parents have split up.

Or you might choose a really dramatic sentence. In *Bad Girls*,
Mandy is being chased by the school bullies when the
story begins, and the first line is: **They were going to get me.**
A line like this will make all your readers desperate to carry
on and find out what happens!

_____

_____

_____

_____

JACKY'S TOP TIP: Decide if you're going to write your
story in the 'first' person, like Jacky often does (so you tell
the story through the voice of your main character) or in
the 'third person' (so you talk about your main character).

GET WRITING!

Now's the really tricky part. Once you've got your brilliant beginning, it's time to start your story! Don't be nervous. The best thing to do is just grab a pen and start. You can always go back and scribble it out later if you don't like it. Lots of famous writers do that!

If you need more space, use extra paper. Your story could be one page long — or three hundred! You could try splitting it up into different chapters, like lots of Jacky's books. And if you get stuck, try reading it all from the beginning again — that might give you a brilliant idea for your next scene!

_____

_____

_____

_____

_____

_____

_____

_____

_____

_____

JACKY'S TOP TIP: If you start getting muddled, you could try writing a story plan, where you decide exactly what's going to happen, in the right order. Sometimes following a story plan makes things a bit easier. It will help you make sure you don't repeat bits of the story, too!

THE GRAND FINALE!

This is where you tie everything together and bring your story to an end. Will you give your characters a happy ending? Or a sad ending to make everyone cry? You might even want to carry your story on, and write a sequel!

Why not decorate your finished story with the handy stickers at the front of this Journal?

_____

_____

_____

_____

_____

_____

_____

_____

_____

_____

_____

_____

_____

_____

JACKY'S TOP TIP: This is a good time to read your story from start to finish. You will spot things that don't make sense, or that you want to change. Most of all, reading your story will give you a brilliant feeling of achievement. You're a writer now!

WHAT'S IN A NAME?

The title of your story is so important. A good title should tell your reader something about the story, and make them want to read it! Jacky often names her books after the main character, like *The Story of Tracy Beaker*, or picks an important theme from the story, like *The Worst Thing About My Sister*.

_____

_____

_____

_____

_____

When you have made your decision, think about what your cover might look like if your story was published! There's space below for you to draw it. It might feature your main character. There are some very handy hints from Nick Sharratt on the next page . . .

TIPS ON ILLUSTRATING!
BY NICK SHARRATT

Nick has been illustrating Jacky's books for over twenty years. He always knew he wanted to be an artist and shares some of his top tips here!

If you want to be an illustrator, you've absolutely got to love drawing! Lots of my illustrator friends knew from a very early age that they wanted to be artists because they just adored drawing so much.

If you want to find your drawing 'style', just try drawing a few pictures and look at what comes naturally to you. You don't need to copy anyone!

I usually start drawing with a soft pencil. That way it's easy to make changes if I need to.

You might need to draw a character twenty times before you're happy with it. Try lots of different hairstyles, colours, clothes and expressions. Just look at how many drawings I did of Floss for *Candyfloss* before I got it right!

FINISH THE STORY YOUR WAY!

A good way to practise your writing is by imagining a different ending to some of your favourite stories. Think about how these books end. Now write your own version. It can be as similar or as different as you like!

she jubs on the tab os they emfirer stat blding and gets her hair done.

WRITE A BOOK REVIEW!

Have you ever written a book review? Try it here! Pick a book by Jacqueline, or any other writer you like.

Title _____

_____

The main character is (Describe them! What do they look like? And what's their personality?) _____

_____

_____

My favourite character is (Explain why!) _____

_____

_____

The story is about (Try to sum it up in just a few sentences!)

_____

_____

_____

The part I liked best _____

_____

_____

I didn't like _____

_____

_____

I would/would not recommend it to my friends _____

_____

My score! (Give the book marks out of five!) _____

_____

YOUR QUESTIONS TO JACKY – ANSWERED!

Lots of Jacky's fans email or write to her with their questions about being an author. Here are some of the most popular.

If you hadn't become an author, what would you be?
I'd love to have been an illustrator, but I'm not talented enough. I'd also like to have my own bookshop!

 What's your best advice for someone who wants to be a writer?
I suggest you read lots — not to copy ideas, but to enrich your imagination and increase your vocabulary. I've never met a writer who isn't a total bookworm.

Which has been the hardest of your books to write?
I think it was Lola Rose — it's such a sad book, though it does have a happy ending. I always try to be honest when I write about troubling subjects, but I don't want my books to be too upsetting.

What's the happiest moment from your career as a writer?
I think it was when a girl from a children's home told me that my books had made her love reading, and my character Tracy Beaker had raised her status with the other kids at school. They thought it was now pretty cool to be in care.

 You're so good at writing — is there anything you're really bad at?
I'm useless at maths and filling in forms, and I can barely use a computer!

JANUARY

It was hard to find a place to write privately.
Sometimes I sat up in the middle of the night
and scribbled in the dark with a stolen
stick of charcoal.

HETTY FEATHER

1 JANUARY we were in the lakes it was really fun

2 JANUARY we are leaving from the lakes

3 JANUARY stay in

4 JANUARY

5 JANUARY

6 JANUARY

7 JANUARY

8 JANUARY

9 JANUARY

10 JANUARY

11 JANUARY

12 JANUARY

13 JANUARY

14 JANUARY

JACKY'S TOP TIP: Try reading your favourite book again, and decide what you liked so much about it. It might give you a good idea for your story!

15 JANUARY

16 JANUARY

17 JANUARY

18 JANUARY

19 JANUARY

20 JANUARY

21 JANUARY

22 JANUARY

23 JANUARY

24 JANUARY

25 JANUARY

26 JANUARY

JANUARY

27 JANUARY

28 JANUARY

29 JANUARY

30 JANUARY

31 JANUARY

NOTES

FEBRUARY

Look kiddo, you write whatever you want in your life story. It's your own book, after all.

THE STORY OF TRACY BEAKER

1 FEBRUARY

2 FEBRUARY

3 FEBRUARY

4 FEBRUARY

5 FEBRUARY

6 FEBRUARY

7 FEBRUARY

8 FEBRUARY

9 FEBRUARY

10 FEBRUARY

JACKY'S TOP TIP: If you can't think of a good idea for a story, try writing your life story, like Tracy Beaker and Hetty Feather. It's good practice and lots of fun scribbling down your favourite memories!

11 FEBRUARY

12 FEBRUARY

13 FEBRUARY

14 FEBRUARY

15 FEBRUARY

16 FEBRUARY

17 FEBRUARY

18 FEBRUARY

19 FEBRUARY

20 FEBRUARY

21 FEBRUARY

22 FEBRUARY

23 FEBRUARY

24 FEBRUARY

25 FEBRUARY

26 FEBRUARY

27 FEBRUARY

28 FEBRUARY

MARCH

My story will be turned into a proper book
with gold lettering and a fancy picture
on the front.

SAPPHIRE BATTERSEA

1 MARCH

2 MARCH

3 MARCH

4 MARCH

5 MARCH

6 MARCH

7 MARCH

8 MARCH

9 MARCH

10 MARCH

11 MARCH

12 MARCH

13 MARCH

14 MARCH

15 MARCH

16 MARCH

 JACKY'S TOP TIP: Always keep a notebook handy, wherever you go. Then if a good idea for a story pops into your head, you can write it down!

17 MARCH

18 MARCH

19 MARCH

20 MARCH

21 MARCH

22 MARCH

23 MARCH

24 MARCH

25 MARCH

26 MARCH

27 MARCH

28 MARCH

29 MARCH

30 MARCH

31 MARCH

NOTES

APRIL

Anne Frank was a brilliant writer.
She described everything so vividly.

SECRETS

1 APRIL

2 APRIL

3 APRIL

Megs Birthday

4 APRIL

5 APRIL

6 APRIL

7 APRIL

8 APRIL My birthday

9 APRIL

10 APRIL

11 APRIL

12 APRIL

13 APRIL

14 APRIL

15 APRIL

Annies Birthday
(My Birthday

16 APRIL

17 APRIL

18 APRIL

19 APRIL

20 APRIL

21 APRIL

22 APRIL

JACKY'S TOP TIP: Try keeping a diary, like India and Treasure in *Secrets*. It's so much fun, and is brilliant writing practice every day!

23 APRIL

24 APRIL

25 APRIL

26 APRIL

27 APRIL

28 APRIL

29 APRIL

30 APRIL

MAY

I've been writing and writing and writing away and it looks like I can't help being a writer. I've written so much I've got a big lump on the longest finger of my right hand. You look.

THE STORY OF TRACY BEAKER

MAY

1 MAY

2 MAY

3 MAY

4 MAY

5 MAY

6 MAY

7 MAY

8 MAY

9 MAY

10 MAY

11 MAY

12 MAY

13 MAY

14 MAY

 **JACKY'S TOP TIP:** You don't have to write at a desk, or on a computer. Take your notebook into the garden, or to the park — or even into the bath! Almost every author has a special place where they do their best writing.

15 MAY

16 MAY

17 MAY

18 MAY

19 MAY

20 MAY

21 MAY

22 MAY

23 MAY

24 MAY

25 MAY

26 MAY

27 MAY

28 MAY

29 MAY

30 MAY

31 MAY

NOTES

JUNE

We're going to be famous one day,
you bet. So I've started writing our
life story already.

DOUBLE ACT

1 JUNE

2 JUNE

3 JUNE

4 JUNE

5 JUNE

6 JUNE

7 JUNE

8 JUNE

9 JUNE

10 JUNE

11 JUNE

12 JUNE

13 JUNE

14 JUNE

15 JUNE

16 JUNE

17 JUNE

18 JUNE

JACKY'S TOP TIP: Why not pair up with your best friend and write a story together? You could take it in turns to write a chapter each — or one of you could write, and the other draw the pictures!

19 JUNE

20 JUNE

21 JUNE

22 JUNE

23 JUNE

24 JUNE

25 JUNE

26 JUNE

27 JUNE

28 JUNE

29 JUNE

30 JUNE

JULY

I wished that I could create a proper comic about Mighty Mart. Then she'd be turned into a TV series and a major feature film and a bestselling computer game.

THE WORST THING ABOUT MY SISTER

1 JULY

2 JULY

3 JULY

4 JULY

5 JULY

6 JULY

7 JULY

8 JULY

9 JULY

10 JULY

11 JULY

12 JULY

13 JULY

14 JULY

15 JULY

16 JULY

17 JULY

18 JULY

**JACKY'S TOP TIP:** You don't have to write a traditional story, if you don't want to. Get creative — try making a comic like Marty! You could even produce your own newspaper or magazine.

19 JULY

20 JULY

21 JULY

22 JULY

23 JULY

24 JULY

25 JULY

26 JULY

27 JULY

28 JULY

29 JULY

30 JULY

31 JULY

NOTES

AUGUST

One of my birthday presents was
a journal. I like to write all my stories
and secrets in it.

MY SISTER JODIE

1 AUGUST

2 AUGUST

3 AUGUST

4 AUGUST

5 AUGUST

6 AUGUST

7 AUGUST

8 AUGUST

9 AUGUST

10 AUGUST

11 AUGUST

12 AUGUST

13 AUGUST

14 AUGUST

15 AUGUST

16 AUGUST

17 AUGUST

18 AUGUST

19 AUGUST

20 AUGUST

21 AUGUST

22 AUGUST

23 AUGUST

24 AUGUST

JACKY'S TOP TIP: If you're stuck with your story, have a little break from it. After a week or two, read through it again. You'll be surprised at how many new ideas you'll have!

25 AUGUST

26 AUGUST

27 AUGUST

28 AUGUST

AUGUST

29 AUGUST

3O AUGUST

31 AUGUST

NOTES

SEPTEMBER

'Please could I write a novel for my project,
Mr Townsend?' I asked. 'I think that's a
brilliant idea, Jacky,' he said.

JACKY DAYDREAM

1 SEPTEMBER

2 SEPTEMBER

SEPTEMBER

3 SEPTEMBER

4 SEPTEMBER

5 SEPTEMBER

6 SEPTEMBER

7 SEPTEMBER

8 SEPTEMBER

9 SEPTEMBER

10 SEPTEMBER

11 SEPTEMBER

12 SEPTEMBER

13 SEPTEMBER

14 SEPTEMBER

15 SEPTEMBER

16 SEPTEMBER

17 SEPTEMBER

18 SEPTEMBER

19 SEPTEMBER

20 SEPTEMBER

JACKY'S TOP TIP: You can find inspiration from lots of places. Why not interview your parents, grandparents, aunts or uncles about their lives? You might discover something interesting that would make a great story!

21 SEPTEMBER

22 SEPTEMBER

23 SEPTEMBER

24 SEPTEMBER

25 SEPTEMBER

26 SEPTEMBER

27 SEPTEMBER

28 SEPTEMBER

29 SEPTEMBER

30 SEPTEMBER

OCTOBER

Now, I considered myself an overly eager writer, but it never interfered with my appetite.

SAPPHIRE BATTERSEA

1 OCTOBER

2 OCTOBER

3 OCTOBER

4 OCTOBER

5 OCTOBER

6 OCTOBER

7 OCTOBER

8 OCTOBER

9 OCTOBER

10 OCTOBER

11 OCTOBER

12 OCTOBER

JACKY'S TOP TIP: Don't worry if it takes a long time to finish your story. It can take me at least six months to write one of mine!

13 OCTOBER

14 OCTOBER

15 OCTOBER

16 OCTOBER

17 OCTOBER

18 OCTOBER

OCTOBER

19 OCTOBER

20 OCTOBER

21 OCTOBER

22 OCTOBER

23 OCTOBER

24 OCTOBER

25 OCTOBER

26 OCTOBER

27 OCTOBER

28 OCTOBER

29 OCTOBER

30 OCTOBER

31 OCTOBER

NOTES

NOVEMBER

I shone at English. I liked it best when
we could make up stories.

JACKY DAYDREAM

1 NOVEMBER

2 NOVEMBER

3 NOVEMBER

4 NOVEMBER

5 NOVEMBER

6 NOVEMBER

7 NOVEMBER

8 NOVEMBER

9 NOVEMBER

10 NOVEMBER

11 NOVEMBER

12 NOVEMBER

13 NOVEMBER

14 NOVEMBER

15 NOVEMBER

16 NOVEMBER

17 NOVEMBER

18 NOVEMBER

19 NOVEMBER

20 NOVEMBER

21 NOVEMBER

22 NOVEMBER

23 NOVEMBER

24 NOVEMBER

 JACKY'S TOP TIP: Sometimes it's good to base your characters on real-life people, like friends or family. It will help you to picture them really clearly!

25 NOVEMBER

26 NOVEMBER

27 NOVEMBER

28 NOVEMBER

29 NOVEMBER

30 NOVEMBER

DECEMBER

You could be a writer too, Hetty Feather.
You have a very vivid imagination
and a gift with words.

HETTY FEATHER

1 DECEMBER

2 DECEMBER

3 DECEMBER

---

4 DECEMBER

5 DECEMBER

6 DECEMBER

7 DECEMBER

8 DECEMBER

9 DECEMBER

10 DECEMBER

11 DECEMBER

12 DECEMBER

13 DECEMBER

14 DECEMBER

15 DECEMBER

16 DECEMBER

17 DECEMBER

18 DECEMBER

JACKY'S TOP TIP: If you really, truly want to be a writer one day . . . never give up!

19 DECEMBER

20 DECEMBER

21 DECEMBER

22 DECEMBER

23 DECEMBER

24 DECEMBER

25 DECEMBER

26 DECEMBER

27 DECEMBER

28 DECEMBER

29 DECEMBER

30 DECEMBER

31 DECEMBER

NOTES

PUZZLE TIME!

Have fun with this wordsearch (hint — all the words you'll find have something to do with writing!).

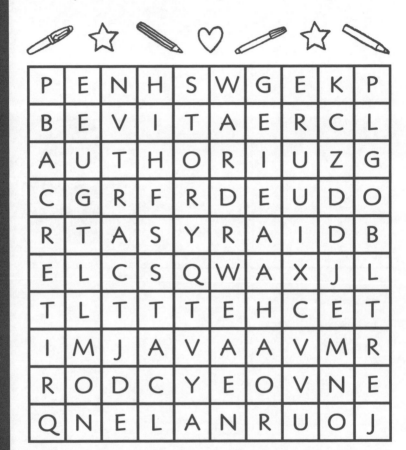

P	E	N	H	S	W	G	E	K	P
B	E	V	I	T	A	E	R	C	L
A	U	T	H	O	R	I	U	Z	G
C	G	R	F	R	D	E	U	D	O
R	T	A	S	Y	R	A	I	D	B
E	L	C	S	Q	W	A	X	J	L
T	L	T	T	T	E	H	C	E	T
I	M	J	A	V	A	A	V	M	R
R	O	D	C	Y	E	O	V	N	E
Q	N	E	L	A	N	R	U	O	J

PUZZLE TIME!

Test how much you know about writing in Jacky's books with this quick quiz! You'll find the answers at the bottom of the last page.

1. What was the name of Jacky's very first story?

2. Which of Jacky's characters are inspired to write diaries like Anne Frank?

3. Hetty Feather loves writing her life story. But which author tries to steal her ideas?

4. What's the name of Violet's favourite author in *Midnight*?

5. What was Jacky's very favourite book when she was younger?

6. Which of Jacky's characters invents a beautiful witch named Mandiana the Magic?

7. In *Double Act*, Ruby and Garnet audition to play twins from a famous story by Enid Blyton. What is it?

8. Which of Jacky's characters is given a very tiny copy of *Thumbelina* as a secret Christmas present?

REVIEWS!

Show your finished story to your family and friends, and ask them to write book reviews. Ask them to be as honest as possible. It will help you work out what you did really well, and what you might be able to improve next time.
Then stick all the reviews here!

HAVE YOU SEEN THIS OTHER GORGEOUS JACQUELINE WILSON STATIONERY?

CHECK OUT JACQUELINE WILSON'S OFFICIAL WEBSITE!

You'll find lots of fun stuff including games and amazing competitions. You can even customise your own page and start an online diary!

You'll find out all about Jacqueline in her monthly diary and tour blogs, as well as seeing her replies to fan mail. You can also chat to other fans on the message boards.

Join in today at
www.jacquelinewilson.co.uk

And watch the brilliant video trailers for Jacqueline's books at
www.youtube.com/jacquelinewilson.tv

OUT NOW!

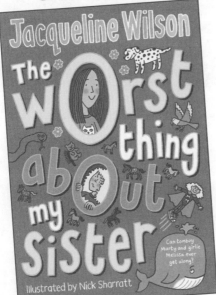

Can tomboy Marty and girlie Melissa ever get along?

NEW BESTSELLER!

AND HAVE YOU READ...

Meet the fiery, feisty HETTY FEATHER!

ALSO AVAILABLE BY JACQUELINE WILSON

Published in Corgi Pups, for beginner readers:
THE DINOSAUR'S PACKED LUNCH
THE MONSTER STORY-TELLER

Published in Young Corgi, for newly confident readers:
LIZZIE ZIPMOUTH
SLEEPOVERS

Available from Doubleday/Corgi Yearling Books:

BAD GIRLS	JACKY DAYDREAM
THE BED AND	LILY ALONE
BREAKFAST STAR	LITTLE DARLINGS
BEST FRIENDS	THE LONGEST WHALE SONG
BIG DAY OUT	THE LOTTIE PROJECT
BURIED ALIVE!	MIDNIGHT
CANDYFLOSS	THE MUM-MINDER
THE CAT MUMMY	MY SECRET DIARY
CLEAN BREAK	MY SISTER JODIE
CLIFFHANGER	SAPPHIRE BATTERSEA
COOKIE	SECRETS
THE DARE GAME	STARRING TRACY BEAKER
THE DIAMOND GIRLS	THE STORY OF TRACY BEAKER
DOUBLE ACT	THE SUITCASE KID
DOUBLE ACT (PLAY EDITION)	VICKY ANGEL
GLUBBSLYME	THE WORRY WEBSITE
HETTY FEATHER	THE WORST THING ABOUT
THE ILLUSTRATED MUM	MY SISTER

Collections:
THE JACQUELINE WILSON COLLECTION
includes THE STORY OF TRACY BEAKER *and*
THE BED AND BREAKFAST STAR
JACQUELINE WILSON'S DOUBLE-DECKER
includes BAD GIRLS *and* DOUBLE ACT
JACQUELINE WILSON'S SUPERSTARS
includes THE SUITCASE KID *and* THE LOTTIE PROJECT

Available from Doubleday/Corgi Books, for older readers:
DUSTBIN BABY
GIRLS IN LOVE
GIRLS UNDER PRESSURE
GIRLS OUT LATE
GIRLS IN TEARS
KISS
LOLA ROSE
LOVE LESSONS

THE JACQUELINE WILSON WRITING JOURNAL
A DOUBLEDAY BOOK 978 0 857 53174 2

Published in Great Britain by Doubleday,
an imprint of Random House Children's Books
A Random House Group Company

This edition published 2012

1 3 5 7 9 10 8 6 4 2

Set in Blueprint
Designed by Becky Chilcott

RANDOM HOUSE CHILDREN'S BOOKS
61–63 Uxbridge Road, London W5 5SA

www.kidsatrandomhouse.co.uk
www.totallyrandombooks.co.uk
www.randomhouse.co.uk

Addresses for companies within The Random House Group Limited
can be found at: www.randomhouse.co.uk/offices.htm

THE RANDOM HOUSE GROUP Limited Reg. No. 954009

A CIP catalogue record for this book is available from the British Library.

Printed and bound in China

QUICK QUIZ ANSWERS:
1. *The Maggots* **2.** India and Treasure in *Secrets* **3.** Mr Buchanan **4.** Casper Dream
5. *Nancy and Plum by Betty MacDonald* **6.** Mandy in *Bad Girls*
7. *The Twins at St Clare's* **8.** Hetty Feather